Contents

Published by the Royal Yachting Association
RYA House, Ensign Way, Hamble,
Southampton, SO31 4YA
Tel: 0845 345 0400 Fax: 0845 345 0329
Email: training@rya.org.uk
Website: www.rya.org.uk
NSSA: www.nssa.org.uk

Introduction

The RYA Youth Sailing Scheme provides an enjoyable and progressive way to learn to sail. Each certificated course provides an opportunity to recognise your achievements.

RYA certificates are a significant achievement. Instructors sign off each skill as you complete it. Once completed, your certificate can be of use in contributing to other areas of your study or activities, such as PE in school, or the Duke of Edinburgh Award Scheme.

The Youth Scheme is usually completed in small dinghies suitable for your size. However, it can also be completed in keelboats and multihulls with some changes to the syllabus (course) e.g. no capsize drill in keelboats.

You can learn to sail well very quickly, provided the equipment is right for you and the challenge suitable. There is provision for guidance and help within the Youth Sailing Scheme, depending on the conditions and what you have to do. In general, you may receive physical help with any part of the syllabus when more strength is required, e.g. on a steep and slippery slipway.

Make sure you can perform all the skills in one course before tackling the next one; otherwise you may waste time re-learning skills, or even fail to complete all of the new course.

In this logbook 'With instruction' means 'Can perform the task with a briefing for the conditions, and physical assistance if neces

In general courses in the RYA Youth Sailing Scheme are of a minimum length of two da an equivalent series of sessions. They may run over a longer period, especially if you h not sailed since your last course. Sailing is sport which gets better with practice, and should try to sail between courses wheneve possible. Practice makes perfect!

Stage 3 is equivalent to Level 2 in the Natic Sailing Scheme. Courses up to Stage 3 ma delivered in single handed or double hande boats, but Stage 4 should involve mainly th of double-handed boats.

Sailors who are unable to complete parts o syllabus due to a disability may still receive certificate, endorsed as necessary e.g. 'ne assistance with capsize drill'.

| Seamanship Skills | Day Sailing | Sailing with Spinnakers | Start Racing | Performance Sailing |

Stage 4

⬆

Stage 3

■ The RYA National Sailing Scheme

⬆

Stage 2

⬆

Stage 1

▨ The RYA Youth Sailing Scheme

Following completion of Stage 4, you are invited to further develop your skills through the Advanced Modules of the RYA National Sailing Scheme. Details are available in RYA publication G4, the National Sailing Scheme Syllabus and Logbook. If you have experience in double-handed boats you may be able to pass directly from Stage 3 to the National Scheme.

If you have partially completed sections of G11/01 you are invited to have the signed sections transferred across to the new logbook.

PRACTICAL

Rigging

Can assist with rigging a boat.

Launching & recovery**

Can launch a dinghy and get under way with instruction.

Can secure boat to trolley.

Can assist with recovery and stowage of dinghy and gear.

Ropework

Can tie a figure of eight and cleat a halyard.

Sailing techniques & manoeuvres

Can be a responsive crew under instruction*.

Can steer when sailing and being towed.

Can steer on a reach and go about (reach to reach).

Understands the effect of basic boat controls.

Understands the basic principles of stopping, controlling speed and getting out of irons.

Can paddle or row (with sprit, paddle or oars).

Can call for assistance.

Clothing and equipmen

Can put on personal buoyancy corre

Is confident in the water wearing pe buoyancy.

Capsize recovery

Understands the importance of stay with the boat**.

SAILING BACKGROUND

Can name basic parts of a boat (i.e mast, rudder, tiller, centreboard, she etc).

Understands what action to take to those in distress.

Understands local hazards.

Understands how to prepare for a t

Clothing and equipmer

Understands personal safety - and what to wear for sailing (including h and footwear).

Meteorology

Has knowledge of wind direction.

*   not singlehanders
**   not keelboats

ALL SECTIONS COMPLETED

Instructor's signature   Centre stam

he end of this introductory course, you
ave a basic understanding of how a
sails, and some experience of steering
handling the boat. Stages 2 and 3 will
plete your introduction to the sport in
stages.

STAGE 1

Attach completed certificate here

This is to certify that

_____

has completed all the requirements of this
award to the standards laid down in the
RYA Youth Sailing Scheme.

SIGNED _____
                                    Principal/Chief Instructor

OF _____
                                    Recognised Training Centre

DATE _____

SPECIAL ENDORSEMENTS _____

_____

Y1

PLACE SIGNATURE HERE

PRACTICAL
Rigging

Can put a boat head to wind for rigging.

Can rig a dinghy.

Launching & recovery**

Understands how to manoeuvre a trolley clear of other boats and overhead cables.

Can launch and recover a small dinghy in an offshore wind.

Ropework

Can tie a round turn and two half hitches and a reef knot.

Sailing techniques & manoeuvres

Can control speed, and stop by lying-to.

Can get out of irons.

Can go about (close reach to close reach).

Can crew a boat effectively*.

Can sail a shallow triangle across the wind under supervision (gybing optional).

Understands the principles of:

The five essentials.

Returning to a beach** or pontoon (offshore wind).

Capsize recovery**

Can be scooped in during capsize recovery*.
or
Can right one type of dinghy.

SAILING BACKGROUND
Sailing manoeuvres

Understands the No Go Zone.

Understands what is meant by winc leeward and gybe.

General

Has knowledge of:

Spars and rigging.

Parts of the sail.

Sail controls and foils.

Offshore and onshore winds.

Telling someone ashore.

The dangers of man made hazards overhead power lines, weirs.

Rules of the road

Has knowledge of Port / Starboard

Meteorology

Understands several ways of finding direction.

Clothing and equipmer

Can choose and correctly adjust a personal buoyancy aid.

Understands what to wear.

*   *not singlehanders*
**   *not keelboats*

ALL SECTIONS COMPLETED

Instructor's signature   Centre stam

he end of this course, you will have a
ـe of sailing skills and background
ـwledge, and be well on the way to being
ـنnfident small boat sailor.

STAGE 2

Attach completed certificate here

This is to certify that

_____

has completed all the requirements of this
award to the standards laid down in the
RYA Youth Sailing Scheme.

SIGNED _____
Principal/Chief Instructor

OF _____
Recognised Training Centre

DATE _____

SPECIAL ENDORSEMENTS _____

_____

Y2

PRACTICAL
Rigging launching & recovery**

Can rig, launch and recover in an onshore wind.

Can reef a dinghy ashore according to weather conditions.

Can store a dinghy ashore.

Ropework
Can tie a bowline, clove hitch and rolling hitch.

Sailing techniques & manoeuvres
Can demonstrate the basic principles of the following:

The five essentials - sail setting, balance, trim, course made good and centreboard.

Sailing on all points of sailing on a triangular course.

Tacking upwind.

Gybing from a training run.

Righting a small capsized dinghy as helm/crew**.

Coming alongside a moored boat.

Prepare for/take up tow from power craft.

Picking up a mooring.

Racing
Understands the course and starting procedure.

SAILING BACKGROUND
Manoeuvres
Understands how to recover a man overboard.

Understands the points of sailing.

General
Understands how a sail works - bas aerodynamics.

Knows basic terminology for use afl (windward, leeward, bear away, luff

Understands the importance of clea communication aboard.

Understands lee shore dangers and in close company with other water u

Understands advice to inland sailors coastal sailing.

Knows the importance of personal s and telling someone ashore.

Understands the dangers of hypothe and the importance of first aid trainir

Rules of the road
Knows the basic rules of the road - Port/Starboard, windward boat and overtaking boat.

Meteorology
Knows how to obtain a weather fore

Understands Beaufort Wind Scale.

Knows when to reef.

Clothing and equipmen
Understands the importance of:

Personal safety equipment.

Boat buoyancy.

Basic safety equipment e.g. anchor, paddle, bailer.

*   *not singlehanders*
**   *not keelboats*

ALL SECTIONS COMPLETED

Instructor's signature   Centre stam

**ge 3 is equivalent to Level 2 in the
tional Sailing Scheme.**

ing completed Stage 3 you will be able to
in any direction and rig and launch your
t. Your skills and knowledge mean that you
regard yourself as a sailor, not a beginner.

STAGE 3

Attach completed certificate here

This is to certify that

_____

has completed all the requirements of this
award to the standards laid down in the
RYA Youth Sailing Scheme.

SIGNED _____
                                    Principal/Chief Instructor

OF _____
                                    Recognised Training Centre

DATE _____

SPECIAL ENDORSEMENTS _____

_____

Y3

PLACE SIGNATURE HERE

PRACTICAL
Rigging & launching

Can rig, launch and recover in any wind direction.

Can set up a boat according to weather conditions using sail and rig controls e.g. mast rake, reefing.

Ropework

Knows the uses of and can tie:

Figure of eight, round turn and two half hitches, reef knot, bowline, clove hitch, rolling hitch, sheet bend.

Sailing techniques and manoeuvres

Can demonstrate:

Sailing techniques and manoeuvres from Stage 3 in a crewed boat.

Communicate effectively as helm and crew.

Effective use of the 5 essentials by helm and crew afloat including use of tell-tales.

Recovering a man overboard.

Returning to a beach,** jetty or mooring safely in any wind direction.

SAILING BACKGROUND

Has knowledge of:

IRPCS.

Beaufort Scale.

Synoptic charts.

Tidal ebb and flow.

Spring and neap tides.

Knows how to recover from total inversion**.

COASTAL (OPTIONAL)

Can apply practical sailing technique manoeuvres on tidal waters.

Sailing background

Can apply the IRPCS afloat.

Has basic knowledge of IALA buoya how to use tide tables and how to fir direction of tidal streams.

*   *not singlehanders*
** *not keelboats*

ALL SECTIONS COMPLETED

_____

Instructor's signature   Centre stamp

Stage 4 certificate means that you have
skills to sail a double-handed boat as
w or helm, and solve a variety of
blems afloat. Passing this course is the
ural entry point for the advanced courses
he National Sailing Scheme.

RYA
youth
SAILING SCHEME

STAGE 4

This is to certify that

Attach completed certificate here

_____

has completed all the requirements of this
award to the standards laid down in the
RYA Youth Sailing Scheme.

SIGNED _____
                                    Principal/Chief Instructor

OF _____
                                    Recognised Training Centre

DATE _____

COASTAL ENDORSEMENT

SIGNED _____

OF _____

DATE _____

SPECIAL ENDORSEMENTS _____

_____   Y4

Once you have learned to helm and crew a small boat, all sorts of opportunities in sailing are open you. As in all sports, practice is essential if you a to improve your skills and the best way to become a good sailor is to sail a variety of types of boats different conditions.

Having practiced your skills one of the best ways to try a different type of sailing is to take another RYA course.

Following Stage 4, you have a choice of Advance Modules in the RYA National Sailing Scheme. All these can be run in two days, but they can take place over a longer period of time. Each course introduce you to a different type of sailing, and m involve other classes of boat, depending on wha available locally.

SEAMANSHIP SKILLS

Learning skills a short step beyond Stage 4; during this course you will polish and test your skills and learn to re-solve problems afloat. The course will give you a solid foundation for the future and enable you to become much more confident and self-sufficient afloat.

DAY SAILING

If you sail at a coastal location you can; explore the local sailing area, as well as developing your passage planning and decision making skills for small boat cruising. Basic pilotage and dealing with windy conditions are also covered.

not share your skills with your friends?
Assistant Instructor award is available to
e with suitable skills and experience - talk
e Senior Instructor at your club.

Further details of the National Sailing Scheme
are available in RYA publication G4, the
National Sailing Scheme Syllabus and
Logbook.

SAILING WITH SPINNAKERS

A very short syllabus which
probably packs the most fun
of all the RYA courses.
Everything you need to know
to enjoy modern, three-sail
boats.

START RACING

The start line for enjoying club
racing. All you need to know
to get round the course and
lay the foundations for
winning.

PERFORMANCE SAILING

Improve your boat handling
and confidence in
performance boats. This is an
opportunity to practice your
helming and crewing and
work on a smooth, fluent
sailing performance with or
without the spinnaker.

youth
friends
buzz

Racing is an exciting and sociable way to develop your sailing. Starting out can be a little daunting, so these notes highlight the key areas you need to consider in learning t race, and give guidance to help make your racing fun and rewarding.

re are a number of ways to go racing:

ILING CLUBS

st racing in the UK is run by clubs, during
evening or weekends. Some larger clubs
have a youth section and many run
ductory race training sessions.

club member you may be able to hire a
, or sail with another member, but in many
s you need to have use of your own boat.
of clubs run regular courses and training
sailors to improve at all levels. They may
host 'open meetings' for a particular class
oat (see below).

s that run youth coaching sometimes are
ted Champion Club status. This means
they have good quality safety, child
ection, policy and run a race training
gramme which enthuses and develops
ng sailors. These clubs have strong links to
RYA Junior and Youth squads.

ASS ASSOCIATIONS

mbers of these organisations sail the same
s of boat. There will be an active
gramme of race meets or open meetings
und the country and a national

championship to decide the best sailor of that
class. Most class members have a home sailing
club, but many travel to attend open meetings.

RYA SQUADS

The RYA squads exist to develop talented
racing sailors across a range of ages. You will
sail the recommended class dinghies, which
include:

Junior Squads (12-16yrs) Optimist,
Topper, Cadet, Mirror.
Youth Squads (16-19) 420, Laser,
Laser Radial, 29er.
Olympic Squads (19 plus) Laser,
Laser Radial, 470 (men and women),
Star, Yngling, 49er, Tornado, Finn.

All squads have specific criteria for selection,
details can be found in the 'Racing' section of
the RYA website. For further information
contact the RYA Racing Division.

These squads are strongly supported
within the Champion Clubs as a nationally
recognised pathway to developing racing
excellence and talent.

GETTING STARTED IN A CLUB

The majority of sailing is run at approximately
1400 sailing clubs across the UK situated on
waters ranging from large ponds to the open
sea. Most welcome new members; you should
talk first to a committee member to find out
about training courses and opportunities to sail.

Many clubs are listed in the phone book but it
may be easier to click 'Clubs' on the RYA
website and search for clubs in your area.

Choosing the right club will be an individual decision but here are some questions to consider:

- Do they run training for novice sailors?
- Is the sailing area safe for novices?
- What classes of dinghy do they race and when?
- How much is membership and what does it include?
- Do I need to buy a boat?

RYA Training Centres and clubs will provide boats when you learn to sail, but to develop your skills you can also sail with someone e̶ or buy your own boat. Sailing with an experienced person is a really good way to learn and many clubs run schemes to introc̶ new sailors into the club.

If you do decide to buy a boat the best way select one is to find out what classes are sa̶ at your club and which boat is best for your size and ability.

WHAT INFORMATION IS AVAILABLE TO HELP ME?

1. RYA Website www.rya.org.uk

As governing body for the sport of sailing, the RYA provides a comprehensive listing of clubs and classes, as well as all the RYA recognised Training Centres, where you can learn to sail.

2. Websites & Magazines

Yachts and Yachting:
www.yachtsandyachting.co.uk
Dinghy Sailing Magazine:
www.dinghysailingmagazine.co.uk

3. RYA publications

The RYA is internationally renowned for producing quality books, films and leaflets to assist sailors at all levels. To access these either phone and ask for a brochure or look on our website: www.rya.org.uk

4. Sailing Books

Amongst a wide range of books, the Fernhurst book series covers various subjects and these can be bought through most chandlers or book stores. The titles are self explanatory and provide a wealth of information about sailing.

DATE	TYPE	HOURS EXPERIENCE		ACTIVITY AND WEATHER CONDITIONS		CENTRE/CLUB
		HELM	CREW	TYPE OF COURSE OR ACTIVITY	MAX WIND SPEED	INSTRUCTOR/COAC

DATE	TYPE	HOURS EXPERIENCE		ACTIVITY AND WEATHER CONDITIONS		CENTRE/CLUB
		HELM	CREW	TYPE OF COURSE OR ACTIVITY	MAX WIND SPEED	INSTRUCTOR/COACH

DATE	TYPE	HOURS EXPERIENCE		ACTIVITY AND WEATHER CONDITIONS		CENTRE/CLUB
		HELM	CREW	TYPE OF COURSE OR ACTIVITY	MAX WIND SPEED	INSTRUCTOR/COAC

www.nssa.org.uk

NSSA exisits to promote sailing as part of the educational experience of young people.

JIN THE NSSA AND TAKE PART IN OUR EVENTS.

Area and Regional Championships and Series.

NSSA National Championships for the more experienced sailor.

NSSA National Youth Regatta Week aimed at young sailors of all levels, but with serious racing on several courses.

Nations Cup. An international competition held in September. Teams are chosen from performances at the Championships Regatta and local events.

Team racing is hotly contested in Toppers, which are provided. Winning teams are invited to represent the NSSA at the RYA Youth Team Racing Championships.

School Sailing Matters - a quarterly magazine for members.

NSSA Handbook, "Sailing Across the Curriculum" - a 'must' for all teachers, trainers, coaches, interested parents and helpers. Lots of ideas and practical guidance.

The NSSA is working very closely with the RYA to promote youth sailing. RYA Training Centre status can be given and administered by NSSA.

NSSA is a charitable trust. Our income is from subscriptions, English Sports grants and fees on advertisements and flyer distribution.

Hon Secretary

Anna Blannin, 49 West Street, Hertford, Herts SG13 8EZ

For NSSA membership please contact:

Barbara Darling, The Honorary Treasurer, 21, Willow Way, Darras Hall, Ponteland, Newcastle-Upon-Tyne NE20 9RF

email: nbdarling@btopenworld.com

RYA *Membership*

Promoting and Protecting Boating

The RYA is the national organisation which represents the interests of everyone who goes boating for pleasure.

The greater the membership, the louder our voice when it comes to protecting members' interests.

Apply for membership today, and support the RYA, to help the RYA support you.

Benefits of Membership

- Access to expert advice on all aspects of boating from legal wrangles to training matters
- Special members' discounts on a range of products and services including boat insurance, books, videos and class certificates
- Free issue of certificates of competence, increasingly asked for by everyone from overseas governments to holiday companies, insurance underwriters to boat hirers

- Access to the wide range of RYA publications, including the quarterly magazine
- Third Party insurance for windsurfing members
- Free Internet access with RYA-Online
- Special discounts on AA membership
- Regular offers in RYA Magazine
- ...and much more

Join now - membership form opposite

Join online at *www.rya.org.uk*

Visit our website for information, advice, members' services and web shop.

full benefits of RYA membership). The RYA will not pass your data to third parties.

☐ **A.** I wish to join the RYA and receive future information on member services, benefits (as listed in RYA Magazine and website) and offers.

☐ **B.** I wish to join the RYA but do not wish to receive future information on member services, benefits (as listed in RYA Magazine and website) and offers.

When completed, please send this form to: RYA, RYA House, Ensign Way, Hamble, Southampton, SO31 4YA

2

	Title	Forename	Surname	Date of Birth		Male	Female
				D D / M M / Y Y			
1.							
2.				D D / M M / Y Y			
3.				D D / M M / Y Y			
4.				D D / M M / Y Y			

Address

Town   County   Post Code

Evening Telephone   Daytime Telephone

email

Signature: _____ Date: _____

3 Type of membership required: *(Tick Box)*

☐ **Personal** Current full annual rate £33 or £30 by Direct Debit

☐ **Under 21** Current full annual rate £11 *(no reduction for Direct Debit)*

☐ **Family*** Current full annual rate £50 or £47 by Direct Debit

* Family Membership: 2 adults plus any under 21s all living at the same address

Please see Direct Debit form overleaf

4 Please tick ONE box to show your main boating interest.

☐ Yacht Racing   ☐ Yacht Cruising

☐ Dinghy Racing   ☐ Dinghy Cruising

☐ Personal Watercraft   ☐ Inland Waterways

☐ Powerboat Racing   ☐ Windsurfing

☐ Motor Boating   ☐ Sportsboats and RIBs

![RYA]

Instructions to your Bank or Building Society to pay by Direct Debit

Please complete this form and return it to:
Royal Yachting Association, RYA House, Ensign Way, Hamble, Southampton, Hampshire SO31 4YA

DIRECT Debit

Originators Identification Number

9	5	5	2	1	3

5. RYA Membership Number (For office use only)

To The Manager: _____ Bank/Building Society

Address: _____

_____

Post Code: _____

2. Name(s) of account holder(s)

_____

3. Branch Sort Code

		—			—		

4. Bank or Building Society account number

Banks and Building Societies may not accept Direct Debit instructions for some types of account

6. Instruction to pay your Bank or Building Society

Please pay Royal Yachting Association Direct Debits from the account detailed in this instruction subject to the safeguards assured by The Direct Debit Guarantee.
I understand that this instruction may remain with the Royal Yachting Association and, if so, details will be passed electronically to my Bank/Building Society.

Signature(s) _____

Date _____

Office use / Centre Stamp

Cash, Cheque, Postal Order enclosed £ _____
Made payable to the Royal Yachting Association

026 | **Office use only:** Membership Number Allocated

tography

r Bentley
n Phipps
d Ritchie
name Forshaw
library
brary

r library:
an Images

racing fun tide
buzz crew skills

energy friends tea

team crew skill

water racing

buzz youth challeng

tide adventur

racing fun buzz sp

The Royal Yachting Association
RYA House, Ensign Way,
Hamble, Southampton,
SO31 4YA
Tel: 0845 345 0400
Fax: 0845 345 0329
Email: training@rya.org.uk
Website: www.rya.org.uk
NSSA: www.nssa.org.uk

ISBN 1-905104-14-

9 781905 104147